The Story of Christmas

Sticker Book

Alex Taylor and Daria Petrilli

© Scripture Union
First published 2012
ISBN 978 1 84427 766 7

British Library Cataloguing-in-Publication Data
A catalogue record of this book is available from the British Library.

Printed and bound in Malaysia by Tien Wah Press.

Illustrations: Daria Petrilli.
Design: Kessell Direction & Design.

 Scripture Union is an international Christian charity working
with churches in more than 130 countries.

Thank you for purchasing this book. Any profits from this book
support SU in England and Wales to bring the good news of Jesus
Christ to children, young people and families and to enable them to
meet God through the Bible and prayer.

Find out more about our work and how you can get involved at:

www.scriptureunion.org.uk (England and Wales)
www.suscotland.org.uk (Scotland)
www.suni.org (Northern Ireland)
www.scriptureunion.org (USA)
www.su.org.au (Australia)

This is the story of Christmas.

Christmas is a time when we remember that
Jesus was born in Bethlehem.

You can read about it in the Bible, in
Matthew chapters 1 and 2, and
Luke chapters 1 and 2.

Use the stickers to help tell this amazing story!

One day, Mary was sweeping her house. As she cleaned, she thought about Joseph the man she was going to marry. Suddenly, an angel appeared. "Don't be afraid!" he said. "You are going to have a baby. He will be God's Son."

Joseph was sad. Mary had told him about the baby and this meant that he could not marry her any more. But God sent an angel to Joseph in a dream. "The baby is from God!" he told Joseph. "Marry Mary and, when the baby is born, you must call him Jesus."

At that time, the man in charge of the whole Roman Empire decided he wanted to count all the people. Everyone had to go back to their home town. Joseph's family came from a town called Bethlehem. So he took Mary with him on the long journey.

The journey was very long. They had to travel about 70 miles. Mary was about to have her baby so they couldn't go very fast. By the time they reached Bethlehem, they couldn't find anywhere to stay. There was no room at the inn!

Finally, they found somewhere to rest – where the animals lived. Joseph sat Mary down on the hay. They had come a long way, and now Mary was about to have her baby!

When the baby was born, Mary wrapped him in strips of cloth and laid him in the manger. Joseph gave him the name the angel had told him: Jesus, which means 'God saves'.

Out on the hills above Bethlehem, some shepherds were looking after their sheep. Suddenly, an angel appeared. "Don't be afraid!" the angel said. "Today a saviour has been born for you!" Then, lots of other angels appeared, singing songs to God.

"Let's go and see the Saviour!" the shepherds shouted.
They rushed off and found Mary and Joseph. They saw
Jesus lying on a bed of hay. They told his parents about
what the angel had said. Mary thought about it and
wondered what it meant.

Far off in the east, some wise men saw a star. It told them that a king had been born. They followed the star, looking for the new king. Eventually, the star stopped over the house where Jesus was. They were excited to find Jesus, Mary and Joseph.

They went into the house. There they knelt down before Jesus and worshipped him. They took out their gifts of gold, frankincense and myrrh, and they gave them to him. They had met the new king. The king who would save the world.

Now you have read the story, why not have a go at retelling it yourself? Move the stickers around as the story goes on. Or how many different pages can you fit each sticker?

Get counting!
There are lots of different things in the pictures in **The Story of Christmas**. Can you count the number of mice? How many coins can you find? What about sheep?

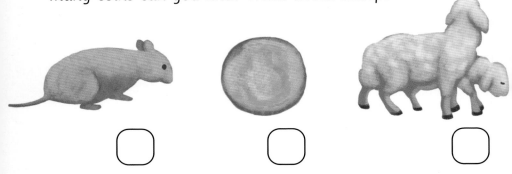

Can you find these things in the pictures inside this book?

How do you celebrate Christmas? Write or draw the different ways here.

What about you?
If you were one of the shepherds, how would you have felt?
Choose one of these words!

Happy   Bored   Not bothered

Excited   Sad   Mad

Scared   Nervous   Interested

                    Overjoyed

What's in a name?
What does your name mean? Find out and write it here:

....

Jesus means 'God saves'. God wanted to rescue his people from the things they did wrong, and Jesus was God's great plan to save. God wants to rescue us too. What do you think about that?

....

Answers:

There are 10 mice
There are 16 coins
There are 19 sheep

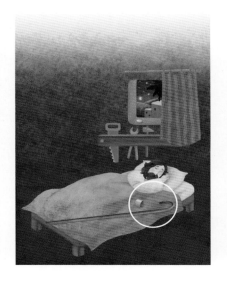